Monsters From

Introduction

The city isn't just a grey place full of concrete and offices.
It's also the home to great, big, drooling beasts.
They're all good at hiding, so you have to be unlucky to see one.

This book covers four of these city dwelling monsters.

The Terrace Tortoise looks like a house.
The Urban Chameleon has a taste for people who deliver pizza.
The Skyscraper Coral hangs out in big buildings.
The Sewer Fluke chases giant rats through the sewers.

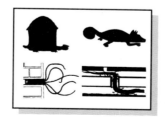

Published by CGP

Contents

The Terrace Tortoise

The Terrace Tortoise

The Terrace Tortoise is the size and shape of a terraced house.

The skin looks like a wall
There are square warts that look like windows.

The shell looks like roof tiles
Unless you look carefully you will think they are just odd tiles.

The top of the skull looks like a door
If someone knocks loudly the monster wakes up.

The tail isn't hidden at all
If anyone sees it they think it's a garden feature.

Large claws hold it firmly to the ground

Their poo looks like bin bags
The nice binmen take it away every Thursday.

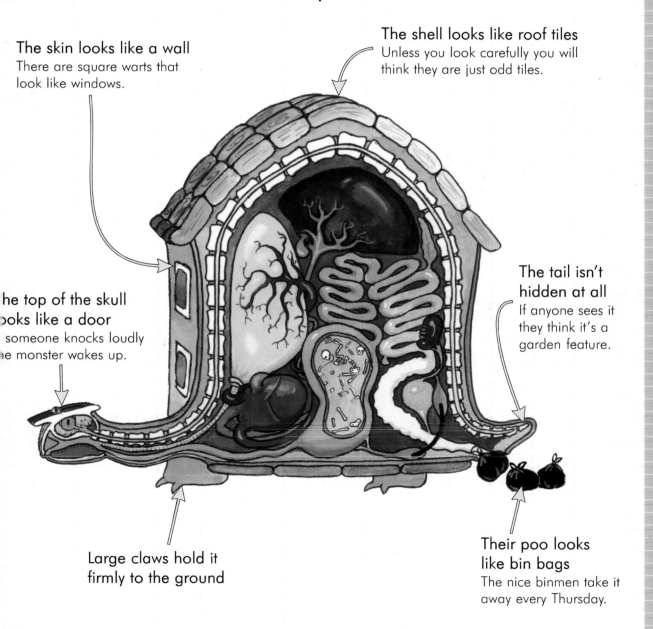

The Terrace Tortoise

Food

The Terrace Tortoise eats salespeople that knock too loudly on its head.

Terrace Tortoises love the taste of salesmen and saleswomen.

**SELL
SELL
SELL**
and try not to get eaten.

Salespeople don't like Terrace Tortoises because:

1) They eat people.
2) They don't buy anything

Enemies

The mighty Space Bluebottle is a giant fly with a taste for tortoise.

These big, blue flies are jet-propelled nasties.

Space Bluebottles only eat Terrace Tortoises if they run out of Skyscraper Coral to eat.

Find out about the Space Bluebottle in the "Monsters from Space" book.

The Terrace Tortoise

Catching Food

sits. It waits. Somebody knocks. They knock again. They get eaten.

(1) **All looks normal**
Salespeople don't see the signs of danger. They see a possible customer, not a deadly tortoise.

signs of danger

e's
ake

(2) **Loud knocking wakes the monster**
If the salesperson knocks for too long they wake up the Terrace Tortoise.

(3) **Gulp**
Once it's awake everything is over in a flash.

- The head comes out.
- The Tortoise swallows.
- No more salesperson.

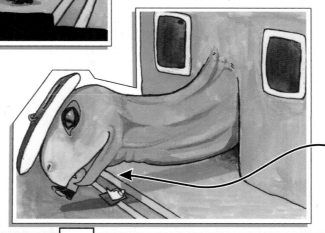

slurp

Life Cycle

It walks a lot when it's young. Then it sits down for the rest of its life.

1. The Terrace Tortoise starts life as an egg buried in a bag full of poo.

2. Binmen and binwomen take the bag to the dump with all the rubbish.

3. The baby Terrace Tortoise hatches. It looks like a small pile of sand. It starts walking away from the dump to find a new home.

4. When it finds an empty house it digs inside. It grows bigger and bigger by eating anyone or anything that comes to the door.

5. As the house crumbles, the Terrace Tortoise eats up the mess to keep the road tidy.

How to Spot One

This checklist tells salespeople how to spot a Terrace Tortoise.

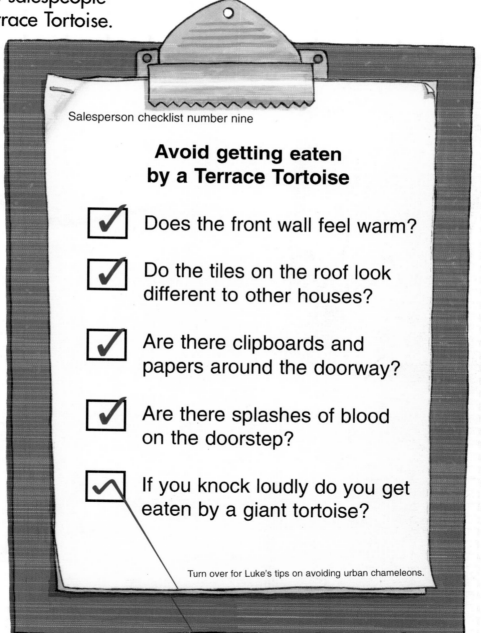

Salesperson checklist number nine

**Avoid getting eaten
by a Terrace Tortoise**

☑ Does the front wall feel warm?

☑ Do the tiles on the roof look different to other houses?

☑ Are there clipboards and papers around the doorway?

☑ Are there splashes of blood on the doorstep?

☑ If you knock loudly do you get eaten by a giant tortoise?

Turn over for Luke's tips on avoiding urban chameleons.

The Urban Chameleon

The Urban Chameleon is a giant lizard that is very hard to spot.

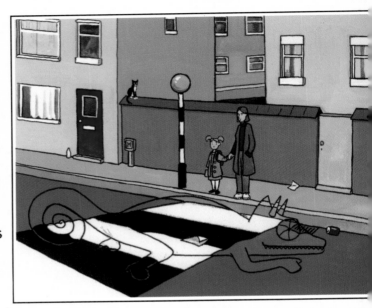

- Urban Chameleons can hide anywhere in the city.

- The Urban Chameleon can change the colour and texture of its skin. It can change to look like part of the city.

- They have long, sticky tongues to catch motorbikes carrying pizza.

KEY

1. The Urban Chameleon
2. A cat
3. A lamp post
4. A girl
5. The girl's mum

The Urban Chameleon

Food

rban Chameleons love eating pizza, pizza delivery people and the bikes they ride.

Juicy bits

Cheesy bits

Crunchy bits

Chewy bits

Enemies

an Urban Chameleon meets a Giant Forest Guinea Pig they fight to the death.

The Giant Forest Guinea Pig looks like a cute ball of fluff. But it's really an unstoppable killing machine.

Find out about the Giant Forest Guinea Pig in the "Monsters from the Country" book.

Catching Food

It sits. It waits. It strikes. It gobbles. Mmmmm... pizza delivery people.

Can you see it?

Maybe it isn't there.

There it is.

The Urban Chameleon strikes again.

The Urban Chameleon

Life Cycle

Urban Chameleons start off life no bigger than a fingernail.

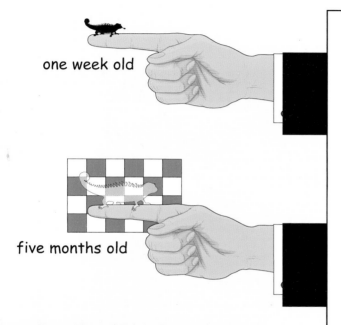

one week old

five months old

As the Urban Chameleon grows up it gets better at hiding.

As a baby it is black. It hides in shadows and eats crisp packets.

As it gets older it blends in more. It hides near takeaways and eats pizza boxes.

When it is two you can just see its shadow. It can hide anywhere it likes.

It eats a balanced diet:
- humans
- pizza
- motorbikes

two years old

The Urban Chameleon

How to Spot One

You can't spot an Urban Chameleon until it attacks.

It takes a hero to spot one and survive.

A hero like Luke Warm...

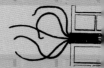

Skyscraper Coral

Skyscraper Coral is like coral from the sea, but 50 storeys high.

Each animal lives in an air vent
It isn't really one monster. Each set of wavy things is a different animal.

The Corals feed through their tentacles
The tentacles suck up traffic pollution and smells from the air.

Each Coral whistles as it eats
Humans can't hear, but Space Bluebottles can.

They come out at night
Their tentacles drift in the night air. They collect pollution.

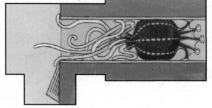

The Coral hides in the daytime
Air vents make a great hiding place.

Dirty office air for lunch
Smelly air comes out of the air vent. The Skyscraper Coral eats the stinky bits as they go through.

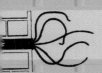

Skyscraper Coral

Food

Skyscraper Coral lives off all the smells in the city.

| Car fumes | Rubbish | Smelly people. |

Enemies

Space Bluebottles land in the night and suck up Skyscraper Coral.

They are big.
They are nasty.
They have jet power

Find out about Space Bluebottles in the "Monsters from Space" book.

Skyscraper Coral

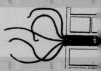

Catching Food

normal skyscraper by day, a monster coral at night.

- Night is when the Skyscraper Corals come out to play.

- Pollution is trapped and sucked up by the tiny hairs along the tentacles.

- As the tentacles wave through the air they make a high-pitched whistle.

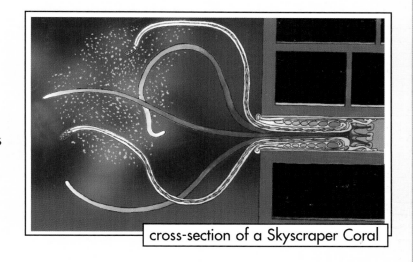

cross-section of a Skyscraper Coral

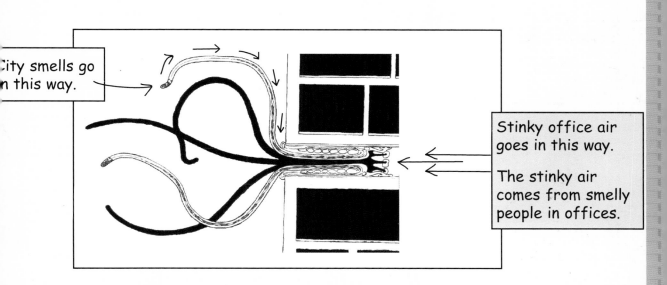

City smells go in this way.

Stinky office air goes in this way.

The stinky air comes from smelly people in offices.

Skyscraper Coral

Life Cycle

Skyscraper Coral lives a peaceful life, whistling high above the city streets.

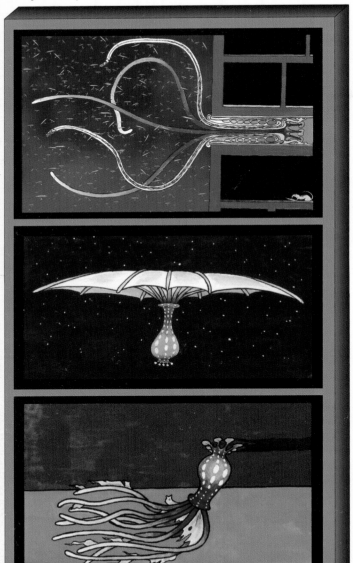

Every five years the Coral release thousands of babies into the air.

The babies are called polyps.

They float off around the city. Some get sucked into air vents.

A ring of suckers sticks them to the inside of the air vents.

They feed on the dirty air from the air vent. They grow to fill the space

Each Skyscraper Coral lives for 72.5 years — or until a Space Bluebottle comes for dinner.

How to Spot One

This is a newsletter about spotting and protecting Skyscraper Coral.

Issue 10   **4th June 2004**

S.C.R.A.P.E. Newsletter
Skyscraper Coral Rescue And Protection Evenings

Skyscraper Coral Spotting Tip Number 321:
Go to a smelly city at night. Then look up.

Thank you for your kind gift of 2 pounds every month.

We are asking our members to give a little more to pay for the giant SWAT plane.

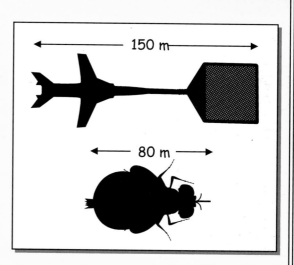

The SWAT plane will protect the coral from those nasty Space Bluebottles.

> **Money raised = £34.52**
> **Total cost = £654,550,000.32**

Save our coral and our coral will save us.

The Sewer Fluke

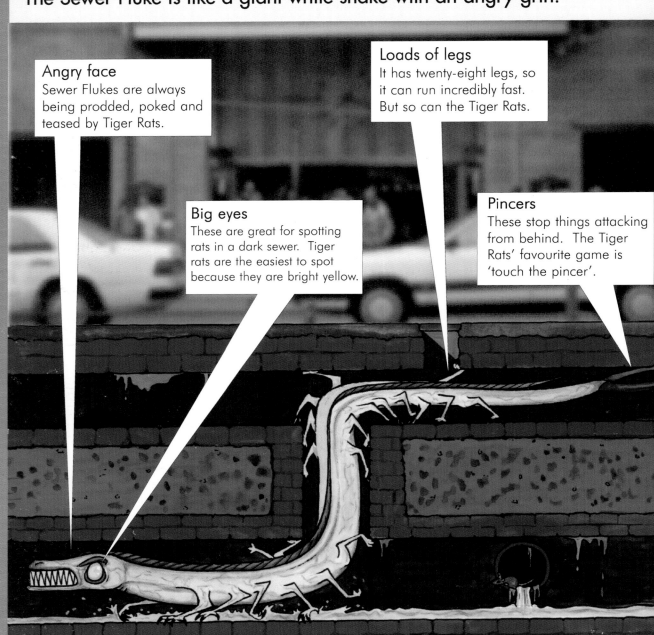

The Sewer Fluke

The Sewer Fluke is like a giant white snake with an angry grin.

Angry face
Sewer Flukes are always being prodded, poked and teased by Tiger Rats.

Loads of legs
It has twenty-eight legs, so it can run incredibly fast. But so can the Tiger Rats.

Big eyes
These are great for spotting rats in a dark sewer. Tiger rats are the easiest to spot because they are bright yellow.

Pincers
These stop things attacking from behind. The Tiger Rats' favourite game is 'touch the pincer'.

The Sewer Fluke

Food

The Sewer Fluke eats normal rats and Tiger Rats.

Normal Rat
Brown and small. They taste like sprouts. The Sewer Fluke eats them but it doesn't like the taste.

Tiger Rat
Bigger and a lot tastier.
They taste like fish and chips.
But they are really cheeky.
They love teasing Sewer Flukes.

Enemies

These little blue fellows don't eat Sewer Flukes, but they do stop them eating.

Blue Tac Tic
It's small, it's blue, it's full of glue.
It lives on the fur of Tiger Rats.
The Sewer Fluke's jaws get glued shut if it eats too many Blue Tac Tics.

If something bites it, a Blue Tac Tic bursts, letting out the glue.

🐛 = actual size

17

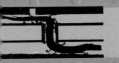

Catching Food

It's easy to catch normal rats, but they don't taste very nice.

Sewer Flukes love the taste of Tiger Rats.

Tiger Rats love to tease Sewer Flukes.

Tiger Rats do get caught an eaten, but they don't care.

They live for the chase.

Look how happy those little guys are.

When Tiger Rats aren't being chased, they play 'Touch the Pincer' behind the Sewer Fluke. It's a dangerous game, so they love it.

The Sewer Fluke

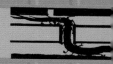

Life Cycle

Sewer Flukes start out life in a post box and end up in the sewer.

Baby Flukes look like maggots. They live in post boxes.

They eat letters and sometimes postmen.

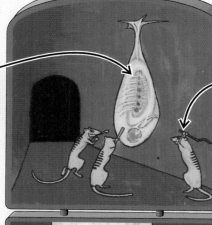

The babies dig down into the sewer and form a hard shell.

Tiger Rats bash the shell to annoy the Fluke.

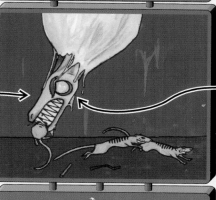

When Sewer Flukes hatch they are already scary and angry.

They love the taste of Tiger Rats in the morning.

How to Spot One

Find some Tiger Rats and the Sewer Fluke will find you.

This is the film poster from the smash hit...

"The Terror Below".

In the film a postman works out how to find a Sewer Fluke:

- Put some Tiger Rats in a net.

- Wait and watch (from a safe distance).

- The Sewer Fluke will come to eat the rats.

The postman then has a choice:

1. Do something heroic.
2. Get eaten for pudding.

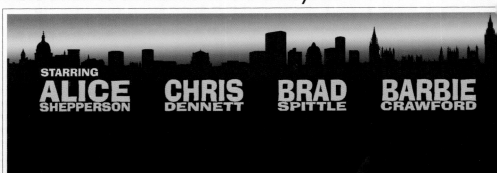

STARRING

ALICE SHEPPERSON **CHRIS** DENNETT **BRAD** SPITTLE **BARBIE** CRAWFORD

City burning above.

Trapped in a sewer.

Dog-sized yellow rats all around.

Those are the least of your worries.

CGP FILMS PRESENT
A MARY SHEPPERSON FILM

THE TERROR BELOW

Glossary

chameleon A type of lizard that can change the colour of its skin.

contents A list of all the pages that are in a book. You can use it to find out which page to turn to.

coral Tiny sea creatures that build large, rocky homes to live in. Lots of these homes make up a coral reef.

glossary That's this page in a book. It lists all the complicated words in a book and explains what they mean.

guinea pig Like a rat, but fatter and with no tail.

hero Brave people who save things like the world. Luke Warm is the hero of page 10.

index That's the next page. It lists everything that's in the book and tells you which page it's on.

introduction In a book, the introduction tells you what the book is about. It's right at the start of the book.

life cycle The life cycle of an animal explains the different stages of its life, from birth to death.

salesperson Someone with a clipboard and a nice voice who tries to sell you things.

tortoise A slow reptile with a shell. One once beat a hare in a famous race. [A hare is like a big rabbit]

Index